LITTLE PILGRIM'S

BIG JOURNEY

JOHN BUNYAN
FULLY ILLUSTRATED
FOR THE NEXT

Hebrews 11:13-16 (NKJV)

These all died in faith, not having received the promises, but having seen them afar off were assured of them, embraced them and confessed that they were strangers and pilgrims on the earth.

For those who say such things declare plainly that they seek a homeland. And truly if they had called to mind that country from which they had come out, they would have had opportunity to return.

But now they desire a better, that is, a heavenly country. Therefore God is not ashamed to be called their God, for He has prepared a city for them.

This book
belongs to a
little pilgrim named:

From:

Date:

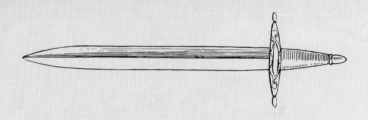

Unless otherwise noted, all Scripture quotations are from
The ESV® Bible (The Holy Bible, English Standard Version®),
copyright © 2001 by Crossway, a publishing ministry of
Good News Publishers. Used by permission. All rights reserved.

Fourth Printing, 2021
Published in Canada by Lithos Kids Press
Printed in China

ISBN 978-1-989975-02-2 Standard Edition

For more books, resources, and a study guide, visit our website:
www.LithosKids.com

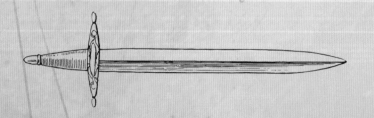

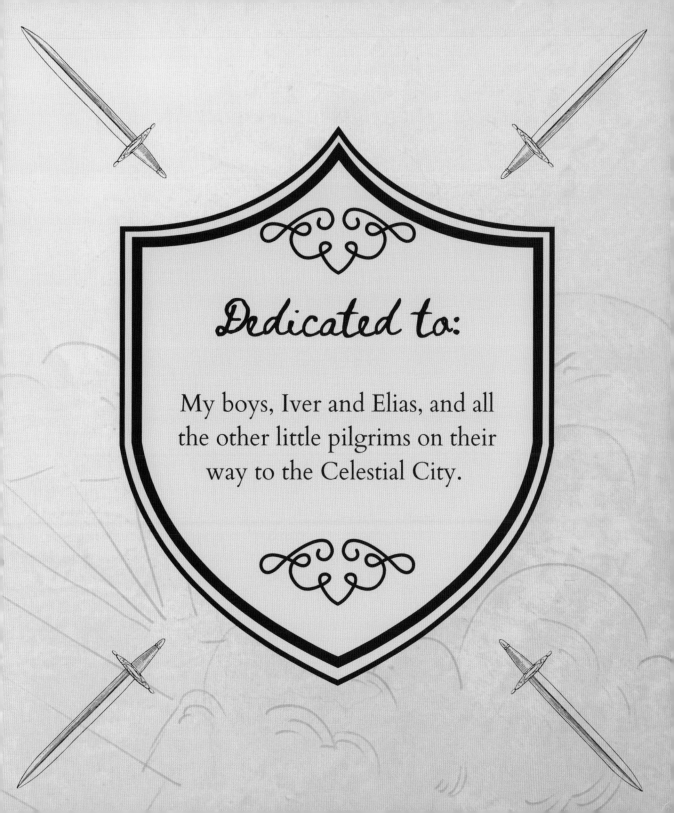

Dedicated to:

My boys, Iver and Elias, and all the other little pilgrims on their way to the Celestial City.

Little Pilgrim's Big Journey

Introduction

In 1661 a man named John Bunyan was put in jail for preaching the Bible. In those days people weren't allowed to teach freely, but had to conform to rules from the government. John Bunyan could have been set free if he promised to stop preaching—but he could not be silent about the truths of God.

He remained in jail for twelve years. He faced great difficulties. But God had great plans for him there. During this time in jail, John Bunyan wrote *The Pilgrim's Progress*.

Some friends told him that it was a silly storybook and he should throw it out. But he printed it anyway. To his surprise, it became famous, and continues to be famous to this day. In fact, next to the Bible, it's the most published and translated book in the world.

This book—*Little Pilgrim's Big Journey*—is based on John Bunyan's timeless tale. It seeks to follow the original storyline closely, while making it easier for children to read and understand.

As *The Pilgrim's Progress* has inspired countless generations of Christians, we hope this book will inspire many little pilgrims to begin their journey to the Celestial City.

What is an Allegory?

The Pilgrim's Progress is not an ordinary story. It was written as an allegory. An allegory is a story with a deeper meaning. All the people and places mentioned in this story are intended to teach us important lessons. (To help parents explain the meaning of this allegory, a short summary is included at the end of each chapter, along with a question guide at the end of the book.)

A pilgrim is someone who leaves home to go on a big journey. John Bunyan believed that the Christian life is like a pilgrimage, with many joys and trials on our way to heaven. *The Pilgrim's Progress* is the story of John Bunyan's experience as a Christian, but it represents the journey of all Christians.

This story vividly explores biblical themes as we follow Christian on his journey to the Celestial City. He faces many obstacles along the way. He meets people who try to help him as well as those who try to harm him.

As you embark on this journey, we pray that you'll be inspired to become a pilgrim and begin your own journey to the Celestial City.

Chapter 1:

The City of Destruction

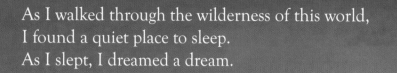

As I walked through the wilderness of this world,
I found a quiet place to sleep.
As I slept, I dreamed a dream.

In my dream,
I saw a boy named Christian dressed in dirty old clothes.
He had a book in his hand and a great burden on his back.
He was crying to himself: "Oh, what can I do to be saved?"

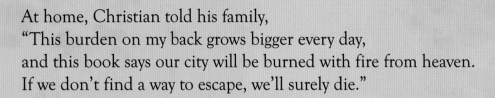

At home, Christian told his family,
"This burden on my back grows bigger every day,
and this book says our city will be burned with fire from heaven.
If we don't find a way to escape, we'll surely die."

But no one believed him.
"You're sick," they said.
"You should go straight to bed."

But the night was as troublesome to him as the day!
Instead of sleeping, Christian lay awake.
He cried and sighed about everything he'd read
in his book.

In the morning, his family woke him
and asked, "How do you feel?"

"Worse and worse," Christian answered.
"We live in the City of Destruction.
We must leave now!"

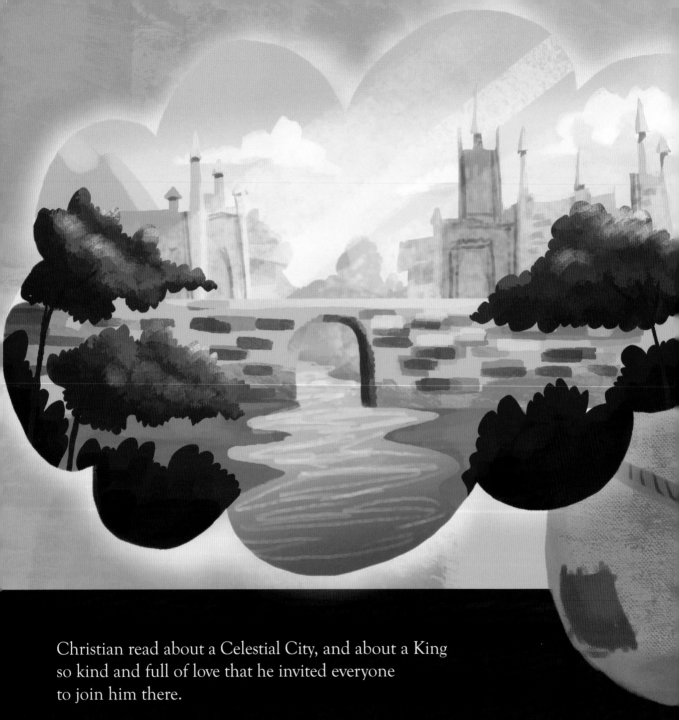

Christian read about a Celestial City, and about a King
so kind and full of love that he invited everyone
to join him there.

"The King has invited us all to the Celestial City,"
Christian said. "Please, come with me!"

But his family became angry.
"Stop telling us these fairy tales!"
They tried to change Christian's mind.
They mocked him, and bullied him,
and sometimes ignored him completely.

But Christian wouldn't stop believing
his book.

Christian took his book to the field to read alone.
He longed to travel to the Celestial City.
He thought, "But what if I get lost on the way?
And how will I travel with this burden?"

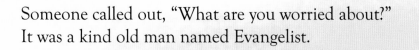

Someone called out, "What are you worried about?"
It was a kind old man named Evangelist.

Christian looked up.
"This book says my city will be destroyed with fire.
I'm scared. I'm not ready to die."

Evangelist pulled a note from his pocket.
It was written by the King himself.
Christian opened it and read:
"Flee from the City of Destruction.
Come find refuge in my city.
I'll keep you safe and secure forever."

Christian asked Evangelist, "Do you think it's true?
Will my city be destroyed? Is the Celestial City real?"

"Yes," said Evangelist. "Every word of it is true.
The King wrote it all, and the King never lies.
Do you want to find the Celestial City?"

"Yes," Christian said, "more than anything!"

Evangelist pointed in the distance. "Can you see that light?
Follow it until you find the Narrow Gate.
When you get there, Good-Will will tell you what to do."

Christian sprinted toward the light in the distance,
right through the middle of town.

People who saw him shouted,
"Where are you going?
Come back, Christian—don't be a fool!"

Some laughed at him and called him names,
and some were sad to see him leave.

Christian didn't even look back.
He just kept running and shouting,
"I want life!
True life!
Eternal life!"

Two boys from the town—named Obstinate and Pliable—
chased after him. "Slow down!" they yelled. "Wait for us!"

Obstinate, who was a stubborn and strong boy, caught up with Christian.
He grabbed Christian by the arm and said, "Come back right now.
Don't be a fool."

"I'm not a fool," said Christian. "And I can't come back, because you live in the City of Destruction.
But I seek an everlasting city. Please, come along with me."

"No way!" said Obstinate. "I could never leave behind all my friends and all my stuff."

Christian answered, "The friends and pleasures you speak of can't compare to the joys I seek. I seek a treasure that can never be lost, or stolen, or broken. Read about it in my book."

But Obstinate refused. "Hush! I don't care about your book. Let's go home, Pliable. Christian has lost his mind."

"Don't make fun of him," Pliable told Obstinate.
"If what he says is true, I'd like to go with him."

Obstinate laughed. "Then you're just as much a fool as Christian.
Have fun searching for your imaginary city." He turned and went back.

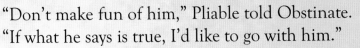

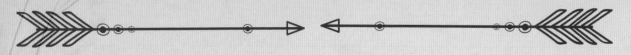

Chapter 1 Summary

In chapter 1 we meet Christian, a young boy who's about to leave the City of Destruction and embark on his big journey to the Celestial City. Christian, as his name suggests, represents all Christians who are leaving this world behind in order to seek a heavenly city (Hebrews 11:8-16).

The book in Christian's hand represents the Bible, which tells him about the coming destruction. He believes everything in it, and he has faith to leave everything behind to seek a greater reward. Salvation begins with understanding and believing God's word (Romans 4:3; Romans 10:9-13).

The burden on Christian's back is the burden of sin. It represents the guilt and shame we feel when we understand how we've disobeyed God. Christian longs to be freed from this burden, but he needs the Evangelist to tell him how this can be done (Romans 10:14-17).

People insult Christian and make fun of him for believing what he reads in his book—just as many people today reject what believers in Jesus tell them about the good news in the Bible (Matthew 5:11-12).

Understanding the Allegory:

1. What does the burden on Christian's back represent?

2. How did Christian respond to the truth in his book?

*A more comprehensive question guide can be found at the end of this book, or can be printed out at lithoskids.com

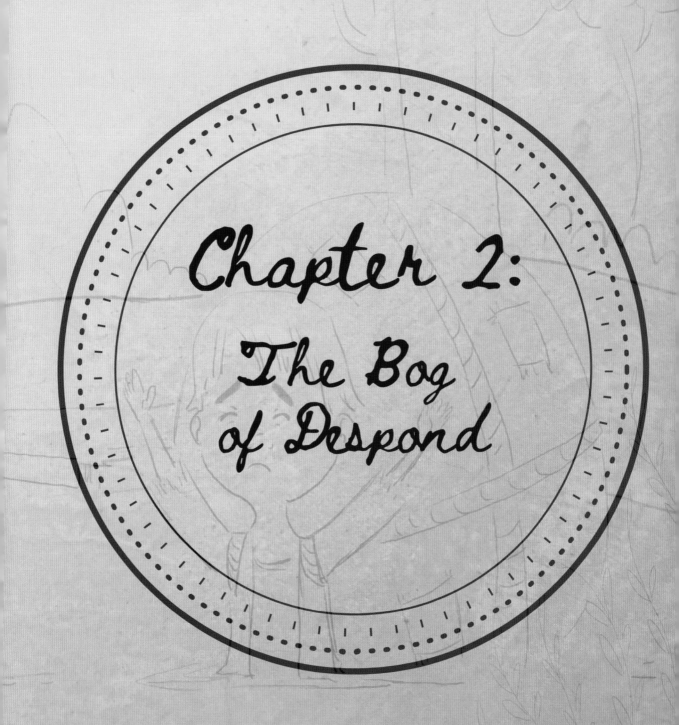

Chapter 2:

The Bog
of Despond

As they kept walking, Christian told Pliable about the Celestial City.
"There will be no sadness there, no more sickness, and no more pain.
The King will wipe all tears from our eyes. Everyone will be happy forever."

"Please tell me more," Pliable begged.

"The King of that city is not like ordinary kings," Christian explained.
"His love for little pilgrims is so great that he's preparing mansions for us.
He'll place crowns on our heads and give us shining clothes to wear."

"Wow!" said Pliable. "But how do you know this is true?"

"Because the King wrote it in my book," Christian answered.

Pliable was amazed. "Why would the King give us all that for free?"

"All the King wants," Christian said, "is for us to believe him,
and follow him, and love him with our whole hearts.
He wants to fill his city with pilgrims from all over the world
so they can know his goodness and enjoy him forever."

They were so absorbed in their conversation that they slipped
and began sinking into a muddy pit called the Bog of Despond.
The more they tried to get out, the deeper they sank.

Pliable screamed, "So this is the happy place you told me about?
I don't believe your King is very good at all!
You can go to the Celestial City by yourself."

Pliable struggled out of the mud and left Christian alone.
Christian sank deeper and deeper into the bog because of his burden.

32

Just as Christian's head sank under the mud,
a strong hand reached down
and pulled him out.

33

"My name is Help," the man said. "The King sent me here
to rescue any pilgrims who fall into this bog."

"Why hasn't the King filled in this bog with dirt?" Christian asked.

"It can't be filled," said the man. "Many have tried to mend it.
And though the King put in steps, many pilgrims don't look for them.
But have no fear. The King is always with you,
and he'll send help when you need it most."

Christian continued alone, thinking about his family and everything he left behind. Then he met an older boy named Worldly, who laughed at him. "Why are you carrying such a large load on your back? You look ridiculous."

Christian said, "A kind man named Evangelist told me to follow the light to where this burden can be removed. He said it can be lifted off only there."

"You've listened to bad advice," Worldly said.
"Evangelist is always leading people astray.
The road he's sending you on is filled with dangers.
You'll meet lions, robbers, and dragons.
You'll be hungry the whole way, and you'll probably die."

Christian sighed. "I just want to get rid of this burden."

Worldly told him, "Then why endure all those dangers?
I know where you can easily be freed from your burden.
It's a little town called Morality. You can invite your family,
and live a long and happy life there."

Worldly pointed. "It's just over that little hill.
You'll meet a man named Legality.
He'll help you take off that burden."

Christian believed Worldly and began in that direction.
But the journey was not as pleasant as Worldly promised.
As he came closer, the hill grew bigger and bigger.
Christian called out, "Hello? Legality, are you there?"

All he heard was a loud *BOOM*
that thundered above him.
The hill grew into a mountain
and began toppling over his head.
Fire and brimstone flew out from it.
Christian was terrified!

Just as Christian lost all hope, Evangelist came to rescue him.

As they moved away from the mountain, Evangelist asked,
"How did you stray so far from the path?
Why did you ignore my instruction?"

Christian felt so ashamed.
"Worldly told me that I could remove my burden here,
and I believed him. I'm so sorry."

Then Evangelist said, "There are no shortcuts to the Celestial City.
There's only one way to remove your burden.
Many people may try to lead you astray,
but you must stay on the path and enter through the Narrow Gate."

Christian rushed back to the path.

He was so relieved when at last he saw the Narrow Gate!
As he came near, he read a sign over the gate that said:
"Knock and it shall be opened."

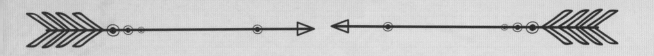

Chapter 2 Summary

In chapter 2, Pliable joins Christian on his journey and is eager to hear about the Celestial City. However, at the first difficulty, Pliable quickly abandons Christian and returns to the City of Destruction. The Bible teaches us about people who accept the word of God at first but then quickly turn away when trouble comes (Mark 4).

The Bog of Despond represents the discouragement a Christian may receive when they begin their journey. They can face fear, or doubt, or discouragement over their sins. The man named Help, who pulls Christian out of the bog, is like the Holy Spirit. God has given us the Holy Spirit to strengthen and help us (Romans 8:26).

The man named Worldly represents people who think they know a different or easier way to remove the burden of sin. The town of Morality is a picture of those who think they can remove their burden of sin by doing good things or obeying rules. Many people in our world believe this. But as we see in the story, this only makes our situation worse (Galatians 3:1-14). There's only one place where our burdens can be removed—at the cross of Jesus Christ (Acts 4:12).

Understanding the Allegory:

1. Why did Pliable turn back to the City of Destruction?

2. What did Worldly tell Christian? Was it true?

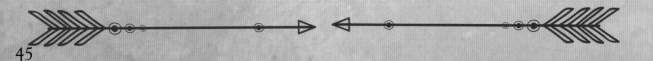

Chapter 3:
The Interpreter's House

Christian knocked and waited,
but he heard nothing.

He was afraid and worried.
"The King may not let me in
because I strayed from the path,
and I'm so filthy,
and my clothes are so ragged."

Christian knocked again.
He called out,
"Are you willing to let
this poor pilgrim in?"

At last, Good-Will opened the door.
"I am willing, with all my heart."

48

Just then several arrows flew through the air.
Good-Will grabbed Christian by the shirt
and pulled him inside the gate.

Good-Will told him about a nearby castle set up by Lord Beelzebub.
"He hates the King and despises little pilgrims," Good-Will said.
"He does all he can to stop them from entering the Narrow Gate."

Christian heard a thud as more arrows hit the door
where he'd just been standing.

Good-Will showed Christian the straight and narrow path.
"This is the way to the Celestial City. It's clear all the way there."

Christian saw the path and asked, "So I can't get lost?"

"The path is clear all the way," Good-Will replied.
"But many other paths cross it. They're wide and crooked,
and they can lead you the wrong way.
The right path is obvious, but it isn't always easiest."

Christian asked Good-Will, "Where can I be freed from this burden?"
His shoulders were terribly sore from carrying it so long.

"Bear your burden a little longer," Good-Will said.
"You must continue your journey
until you come to the Place of Deliverance.
Only there can your burden be removed."

"But first you must go to the house of the Interpreter."
Good-Will explained. "He'll show you excellent things
to help you on your journey."

"Welcome, little pilgrim," the Interpreter said.
"The King placed me here to prepare you
for the many challenges you will face
on your journey."

They entered a dirty room.
Interpreter asked a man to sweep the room,
which filled the room with dust.
Christian began to cough.

Interpreter asked another helper
to sprinkle the room with water.
This made the dust settle to the floor,
so it could be easily cleaned.

"The dust is our sin," Interpreter said, "and the sweeping broom is like trying to fix our sin by following all sorts of rules. The sprinkled water is like the King's mercy and grace, which are the only way to remove dirt from our lives. It is not through our efforts that we become clean, but only by trusting in the King to purify us."

In the next room, Christian saw two boys named Passion and Patience.
They were getting gifts, but were told to wait a year to receive them.
Passion couldn't sit still. "Give it to me now!" he whined.
But Patience sat quietly.

Passion finally got his gifts, but they were soon broken.
Patience waited happily, and was given gifts that can never break.

Interpreter explained:
"Passion is like people who want everything now.
Patience is like those who trust the King and are willing to wait.
Their reward will last forever."

Then Christian saw a fire. A wicked man poured water on it,
but the fire would not go out. Behind the wall was a kind and gracious man
who kept the fire burning with oil.

"What does this mean?"
Christian asked.

"The fire," said Interpreter,
"is like the love pilgrims have
for the King."

And he said, "The man pouring water is like Lord Beelzebub, who always tries to hinder pilgrims.
But the man pouring oil is like the King's Son, who helps pilgrims on their journey."

Interpreter took Christian to one last room,
which opened up to show a castle
guarded by soldiers.

Some people were afraid to enter, but one man ran forward
with all his might, attacking the guards with his sword.
When he reached the palace gates,
the angels above called out in their sweet voices,
"Come in, come in! Eternal glory you shall win."

Christian said, "I know the meaning of this!
Many people want to enter the Celestial City,
but they fear what it may cost them, so they stay back.
Only those who go on in faith and perseverance will arrive."

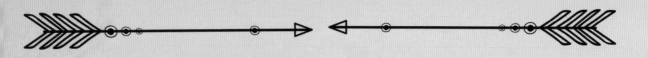

Chapter 3 Summary

In chapter 3, Christian is welcomed into the Narrow Gate by Good-Will. This is a picture of Jesus, who welcomes anyone who will come to him in faith. Even though Christian felt like he wasn't worthy, Good-Will accepted him.

Jesus spoke about the Narrow Gate in Matthew 7:13-14: "Enter by the narrow gate. For the gate is wide and the way is easy that leads to destruction, and those who enter by it are many. For the gate is narrow and the way is hard that leads to life, and those who find it are few."

Jesus calls us to take the narrow road, which is often more difficult than the wide road. There will be times where Christians need to make difficult decisions and sacrifice things in order to turn from sin and follow Jesus (Matthew 16:24).

Christian also goes to the house of Interpreter, who represents people who teach the Bible, such as pastors, parents, and Sunday School teachers. They help us understand God's truth so we can continue in the Christian journey. We need good teachers to equip us for life in this world (Ephesians 4:11-16)

Understanding the Allegory:

1. Why was Christian worried he wouldn't be welcomed into the Narrow Gate? How did Good-Will respond to him?

2. What was one of the lessons Interpreter taught Christian?

Chapter 4:
The Place
of Deliverance

Christian ran, longing to make it to the Place of Deliverance.
On both sides of the path were great high walls called Salvation.
His legs were sore, and his body ached under his burden.
He was determined to be free from it at last.

He ran until he reached a hill, where he saw a large wooden cross.
His book told him that the King's Son had died on this cross
so that little pilgrims could be freed from their burdens.

Christian's eyes filled with tears. He thought how much
it must have hurt the King to send his only Son to die,
and how much pain the Son must have endured while dying.

Christian stood in wonder. "I lived my whole life
in the City of Destruction. I continually disobeyed the King.
I never once thanked him or showed him any love.
I'm a poor little pilgrim in filthy clothes.
Why would he do this for me?"

As he drew nearer to the cross, the straps on his shoulders snapped, and the huge load fell off his back. It rolled down the hill, picking up greater speed until it fell into a large pit—never to be seen again.

Christian beamed with joy—he was finally free!
His heart was full of love for the King's Son.
"He died, so I can live.
He was broken, so I can be made whole.
He endured the worst, to give me the best."

Christian sang a new song:

*I came to the cross
with the burden of sin,
for none could remove
all the guilt held within.*

*What a wonderful day!
I've been covered by grace!
For the King sent his Son
To die in my place.*

*At the cross I am free.
Here my burden's released.
Here my shame has been
thrown in a bottomless sea.*

Then three Shining Ones appeared and said,
"Now you can know true and lasting peace."

The first one said, "All your sins are washed away."

The second removed Christian's filthy old clothes
and exchanged them for new clothes, clean and beautiful.

The third gave him a scroll with a seal on it, and said,
"Keep this with you on your journey,
and present it at the Celestial City.
It's a reminder that you'll always be welcome there,
and it's proof that you're one of the King's pilgrims."

As Christian continued his journey, his steps were lighter,
and the world around seemed brighter.

At the bottom of a hill, Christian saw three sleepy boys
with chains on their feet.
Their names were Simple, Slothful, and Presumption.

He called to them, "Wake up! You aren't safe here.
The Prince Beelzebub could find you and capture you.
Come with me, and I'll help you remove your chains."

"There's no danger here,"
Simple said.

Slothful yawned and said,
"Let me sleep a little longer."

And Presumption said,
"Every tub must stand
on its own bottom."

Christian wondered why
they didn't want his help.
He continued on by himself.

As Christian walked along the path
he saw two boys jump over the wall of Salvation beside him.
One was named Formalist. The other was named Hypocrisy.
Christian asked them, "What are you doing?"

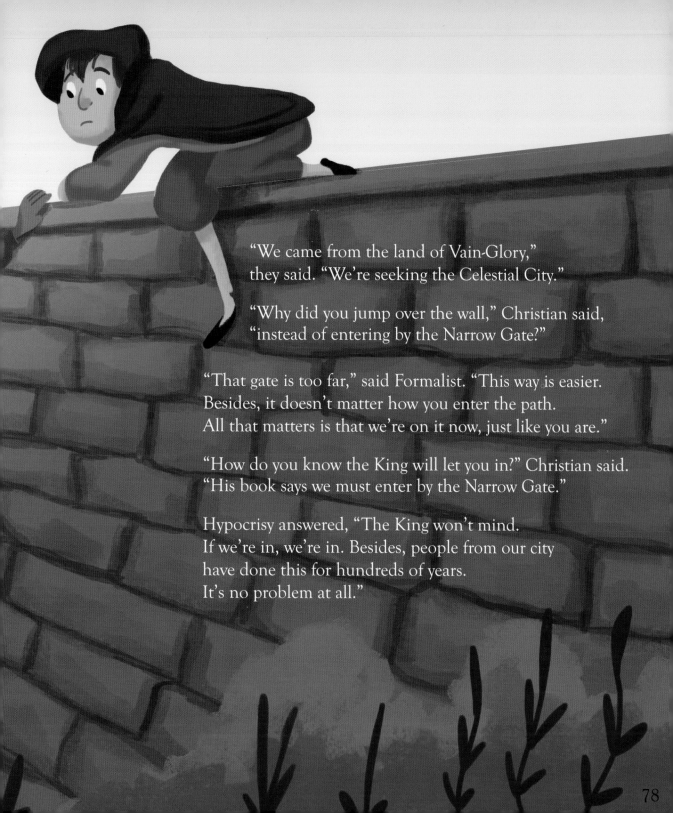

"We came from the land of Vain-Glory,"
they said. "We're seeking the Celestial City."

"Why did you jump over the wall," Christian said,
"instead of entering by the Narrow Gate?"

"That gate is too far," said Formalist. "This way is easier.
Besides, it doesn't matter how you enter the path.
All that matters is that we're on it now, just like you are."

"How do you know the King will let you in?" Christian said.
"His book says we must enter by the Narrow Gate."

Hypocrisy answered, "The King won't mind.
If we're in, we're in. Besides, people from our city
have done this for hundreds of years.
It's no problem at all."

"But where's your scroll?" Christian asked.

Formalist said, "Do you think you're so special because you have a scroll? The King doesn't care about silly things like that."

Christian answered, "I used to wear rags, and I was doomed for destruction. But the King saved me. He gave me this scroll to remind me that he'll welcome me into his city."

Formalist laughed. "You can keep your little scroll. I'm not in rags like you were, and I'm not in any danger. The King will let me in when he hears of my good reputation."

"Yes, indeed," said Hypocrisy. "I'm sure the King will be very impressed with us. We're much better off than this poor little pilgrim."

Christian saw that the narrow path led up a steep hill.
There were two other paths, one on each side of the hill.
Both looked much easier and wider than his path.
Christian remembered his instructions from Evangelist
to always stay on the narrow path.

But Formalist and Hypocrisy said to him,
"That path looks far too difficult. Look!
The King has given us better paths to take."

Christian warned them. "No! Can't you see?
Those paths lead to danger and destruction.
Don't go!"

But the two boys didn't listen.
Formalist took the path to the left,
and became lost in a dark forest.
Hypocrisy took the path to the right.
He tripped into a steep valley,
and couldn't find his way back up.

Chapter 4 Summary

In chapter 4, Christian is freed from his burden at last. This represents the joy and freedom to be found when a person understands this truth: "As far as the east is from the west, so far has he removed our transgressions from us" (Psalm 103:12).

Christian's burden could only be removed at the Place of Deliverance. It is only at the cross that we can be freed from the burden of sin, because Jesus is the only one who can take our guilt and pay the penalty for our sin (2 Corinthians 5:21).

Christian is met by three Shining Ones who give him new clothes and a scroll. The clothes represent being covered in the perfect righteousness of Jesus. The scroll represents the security believers have, being sealed for the day of salvation (Ephesians 1:13).

As Christian continues, he meets Simple, Slothful, and Presumption. They represent those who have no desire or care for spiritual things. They refuse to change, and they're unaware of the danger they're in (Ephesians 5:14).

Lastly, Formalist and Hypocrisy are those who pretend to be good and act like they're upright people, but who really don't know God or want to follow his word (Luke 12:1-3).

Understanding the Allegory:
1. What happened to Christian's burden at the Place of Deliverance?
2. Why is Jesus the only one who can take our burden away?

Chapter 5:

The Palace Beautiful

Christian continued up the difficult hill. He knew
that the King's way, though hard, was always best.
Christian was eager to reach the top,
but the higher he climbed, the steeper it became.
He soon had to crawl on his hands and knees.
He wondered: "Will I ever make it to the top?"

Christian was so sore and tired,
he worried he might collapse
and fall down the hill.

To his relief, he came across
a shaded seat with a beautiful arbor.
The King had made this place
to give little pilgrims rest
on the difficult hill.

Christian lay down,
and pulled the scroll from his pocket
to read the message from the King.
He looked at the beautiful clothes
the King had given him.
He smiled, then drifted
into a deep sleep.

Christian heard a voice in his dream:
"Look to the ant, you sluggard.
Consider his ways and be wise."
He'd slept too long—it was nearly dark!
He panicked, and hurried toward the top of the hill.

Two boys named Timorous and Mistrust
came running down the hill.

Christian asked them, "Why are you going this way?
The Celestial City is the other direction."

"We tried to make it to the Celestial City,"
they answered, "but the farther we go,
the more dangers we meet. Lions are on the path—
big, ferocious lions. We're turning back."

As Christian kept going, he wondered:
"If I go forward, I may be attacked by lions.
If I go back to the City of Destruction,
I'll certainly die there. What should I do?"

Christian reached to find the scroll he had been given.
He couldn't find it. "Oh, no! Where could it be?
Will the King let me in without it?"

Then he remembered the place
where he'd slept.
"Maybe I dropped it there.
I'm such a fool for sleeping so long
while there was daylight.
Now I may never find my scroll!"

Christian reached the arbor
and searched in the darkness.
Then he saw something
glimmering in the moonlight.
"My scroll!" Christian rejoiced.
He picked it up
and clutched it to his chest.

But his joy turned to fear as he remembered
what the boys had said. "Did they really see lions?
It's so dark now, and lions will be able
to sneak up on me."

Christian saw a beautiful palace, and walked toward it.
He hoped to find a safe place to sleep for the night.

But there were the lions—guarding the pathway!
He wanted to run, but he was frozen in fear.
He heard a voice call out from the palace:
"Do not lose heart. The lions cannot hurt you.
They were placed here to test your faith.
If you stay on the narrow path,
they'll never reach you."

Christian continued with small steps. He was trembling.
The lions roared and growled as he passed,
but now he saw that they were chained.

At the gate, he was greeted by Watchful. Christian asked,
"Sir, what house is this? May I stay here for the night?"

"This is the Palace Beautiful," Watchful answered.
"It was built by the King to help pilgrims on their journey."

Christian was delighted.
"I knew the King wouldn't leave me on my own!
He has helped me all along the way."

Inside, Christian met Discretion,
Prudence, Piety, and Charity.
He told them all about his journey so far.

Prudence asked him, "After so much trouble,
why do you still want to go to the Celestial City?"

"Because I want to meet the King,"
said Christian. "And I want to see his Son
who loved me so much that he died for me.
His book tells me there's no more death in that city,
and no more crying, or pain, or sin, or corruption."

Charity asked Christian, "Where's your family?
Why did they not come?"

"Oh, how badly I wanted them to come!"
Christian answered. "I tried to convince them,
but they didn't believe my book."

Christian was tired and hungry, so the four women brought out a wonderful meal for him.

During the meal, they talked about the King. They told Christian how the King's Son left the Celestial City to seek poor pilgrims. He even became a pilgrim himself, and walked the King's path without ever turning away to the wide and crooked paths.

They told him of the great battle with Beelzebub, and how the King's Son died to defeat him— but rose again victorious.

All this made Christian love the King even more.

As Christian thought about the King's Son,
his heart was full of joy. He slept soundly that night.

When he woke, the women showed him the armory.
It was filled with weapons from the King for pilgrims
to use in fighting any enemies along the path.
Christian looked at swords, shields,
helmets, and breastplates.
He wondered whether someday
he might need to wear this armor.

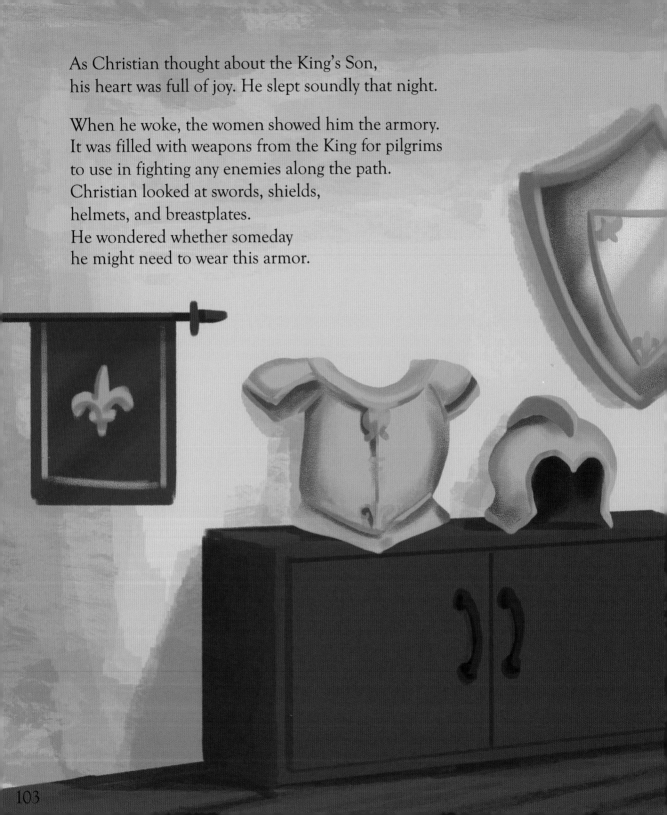

Chapter 5 Summary

In chapter 5, Christian ascends the Hill of Difficulty. This hill represents the trials and difficulties a believer will face. Often when someone becomes a Christian, their life becomes more difficult, not easier. They have to make hard decisions, change sinful habits, and their family or friends may be angry with them (2 Timothy 3:12).

Christian reaches a place of rest, but he sleeps too long. God gives us rest in all our difficulties, but we're told to not be lazy (Proverbs 6:6-12). Sometimes difficulties and discouragement can make us want to give up, but we must continue with God's help (Ephesians 5:15-16).

Christian arrives at the Palace Beautiful. Here he's met by four women who encourage him on his journey. Although there are trials in the Christian life, there are also far greater joys. One of those joys is fellowship with other believers, who provide timely advice and affirmation. The Palace Beautiful represents the church (1 Thessalonians 5:11).

The armor that Christian sees represents the armor of God listed in Ephesians 6:10-20. Christians will enter into spiritual battle and must be prepared with the truths of the gospel.

Understanding the Allegory:

1. What does the Hill of Difficulty represent?
2. How did the women at the Palace Beautiful help Christian?

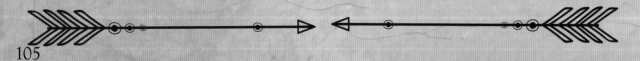

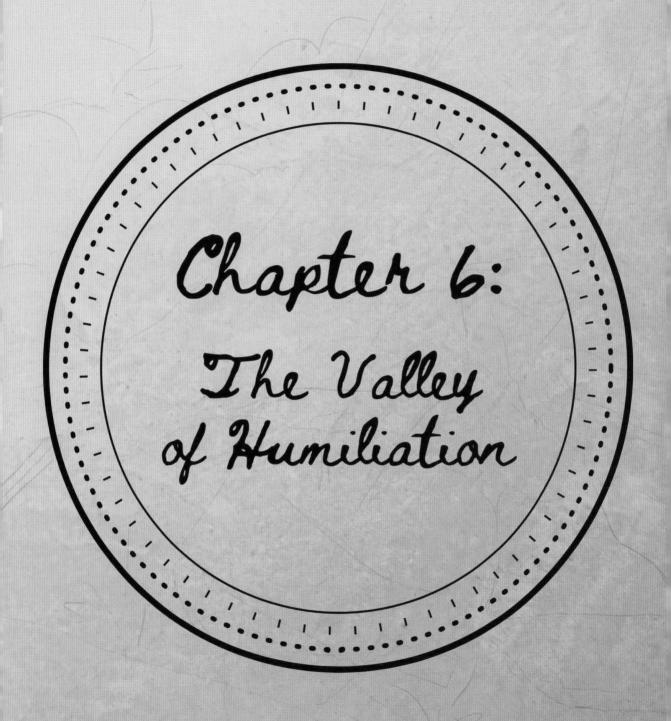

Chapter 6:

The Valley
of Humiliation

Christian saw many treasures within the palace,
and out his window he could see Immanuel's Land.
Christian wished to stay with his new friends,
but he knew he must continue to the King's city.

As Christian set out, the women gave him
a full set of armor for facing any enemies on the path.
They encouraged him on his way.

So Christian descended
into the Valley of Humiliation.
Dark clouds filled the sky,
and he saw a foul fiend flying over the field to meet him.

He knew that it must be Apollyon.

Christian was terrified. He wondered if he should turn
and run. But he had no armor protecting his back,
and Apollyon could easily attack him there.

Christian had never seen anything so monstrous.
Apollyon had thick scales, and wings like a dragon,
and huge, sharp teeth. He was full of fire and smoke.
Apollyon glared at Christian.
"Where do you think you're going?"

"To the Celestial City," Christian said bravely.
"I've come from the evil City of Destruction."

"Well, I am lord of the City of Destruction,"
said Apollyon. "You must return to serve me again."

"I will never go back," Christian replied.
"I serve the true King now, and I follow his path."

Apollyon laughed.
"But you don't really serve the King. You disobeyed him many times.
First you fell into the Bog of Despair, then you strayed from the path.
You were lazy and slept too long, and almost turned back
when you saw the lions. You don't seem to love the King at all."

"All this is true," said Christian, "and much more that you left out.
But the Prince whom I serve is merciful and ready to forgive
all who turn to him."

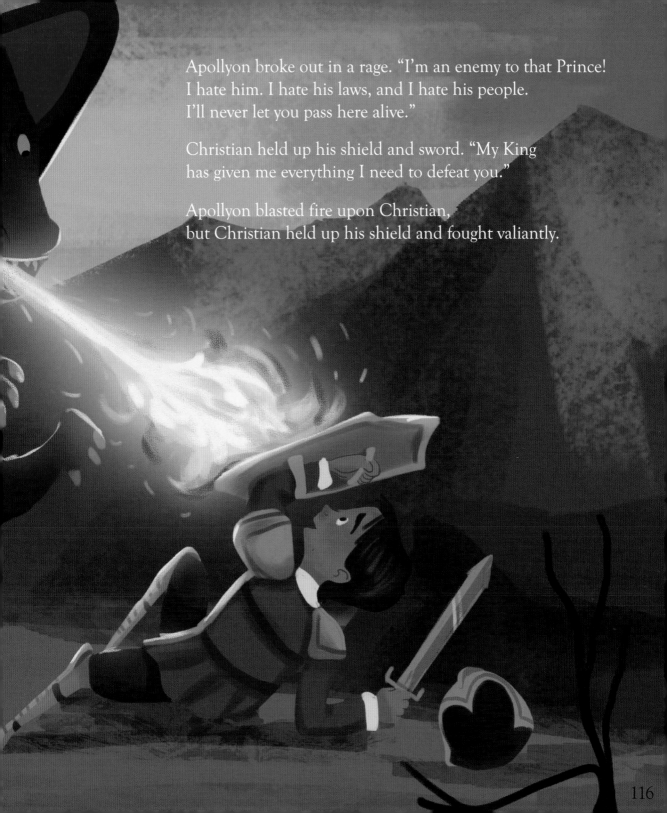

Apollyon broke out in a rage. "I'm an enemy to that Prince!
I hate him. I hate his laws, and I hate his people.
I'll never let you pass here alive."

Christian held up his shield and sword. "My King
has given me everything I need to defeat you."

Apollyon blasted fire upon Christian,
but Christian held up his shield and fought valiantly.

They fought for hours, and Christian grew weary.
Apollyon knocked him to the ground,
and the sword fell from his hand.
"I'll finish this fight now," Apollyon said.

Apollyon raised himself over Christian
to strike one last deadly blow. Christian picked up his sword
and lifted it with all his strength. He said,
"Rejoice not against me, my enemy! When I fall,
I shall arise." He thrust his sword into Apollyon's chest.

Apollyon was wounded. Then Christian struck him again.
"Yes," said Christian, "in all these things
we are more than conquerors through him who loved us!"

At this last blow, Apollyon let out a terrible roar.
Stretching out his wings, he flew away.

118

The battle was finished, and Christian said,
"I will give thanks to the King, who delivered me
from Apollyon's attacks."

Christian heard a voice above: "Do not fear,
for I am with you; do not be dismayed, for I am your God.
I will strengthen you and help you;
I will uphold you with my righteous right hand."

A peace came over Christian,
and though Apollyon had wounded him,
he felt strengthened again for his journey.

Christian continued through the valley with his sword drawn, wondering if another enemy might be waiting for him. Suddenly two boys ran toward him shouting, "Back, go back! Turn around!"

Christian was startled, and said, "What are you running from?"

"From the Valley of the Shadow of Death," they answered.
"It's pitch black, and full of howling and yelling—
the most dreadful place we've ever seen."

But Christian looked ahead. "This is the way to my desired haven,"
he said. "I must pass through it to reach the Celestial City.
I will continue onward and trust the King to guide me."

Christian's pathway become more and more narrow,
with a deadly drop on each side. The valley was so dark
that sometimes Christian couldn't see where he was stepping.
He feared he would slip and fall to his death.
He sighed and groaned as he went on.
Would he ever see the light of day again?

At times he thought he saw the shadow of some evil creature.
He thought he heard lies being whispered in his ears:
"You're all alone. The King has forgotten you.
You'll never make it to the Celestial City."

Then Christian heard terrible sounds arising from the pit.
He saw huge flames and plumes of smoke spewing out of it.
Christian cried out, "O Lord, deliver my soul from this distress!"

He thought to turn back, but he remembered
how he'd already overcome so many dangers.
He pressed forward, trembling with each step.

Now when he became afraid, he remembered to shout,
"I will walk in the strength of the Lord God."
And he heard what sounded like another boy's voice:
"Even though I walk through the valley of the shadow of death,
I will fear no evil, for you are with me."
This gave him courage to press on through the dark valley.

Chapter 6 Summary

In chapter 6, Christian battles against Apollyon. This battle represents the spiritual battle that all Christians are in. At first Apollyon mentions all of Christian's failures. Satan is called the Accuser in the Bible (Revelation 12:10). That means he tries to make us feel ashamed as we remember all the bad things we've done. He tries to convince us that God won't forgive us.

Christian is able to withstand Apollyon's attacks with the Armor of God (Ephesians 6:10-20). The Helmet of Salvation reminds us that our salvation and righteousness come from Jesus, not from us. The Shield of Faith is our faith in God. We are protected from the attacks of the enemy when we trust in God's power to save us.

Christian ultimately defeats Apollyon with the Sword of the Spirit, which is the word of God. The word of God is able to slice through lies and bring us to victory. It's the only weapon given for our attacks (2 Timothy 3:16-17).

David speaks in Psalm 23 of the valley of the shadow of death. This valley represents fear. Christians can trust God even in dark and scary places, even when we are afraid that we may die. We can believe God's word when others speak lies into our ears. God's word gives us courage to face our fears.

Understanding the Allegory:

1. What does Apollyon say to discourage Christian?
2. How does Christian make it through the dark valley?

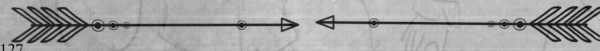

Chapter 7:

Vanity Fair

When Christian came into the light, he rejoiced! He'd made it through the dark valley— though it was full of traps set by the evil Lord Beelzebub.

He saw another little pilgrim running ahead. Christian recognized him. This was Faithful, his neighbor from the City of Destruction.

Christian called out, "Faithful, wait for me! I'll join you!" Faithful shouted back, "I can't stop! I must continue to the Celestial City!"

Christian ran as fast as he could to catch up. When he reached Faithful, he ran past him and said, "Aha! Now I'll get there first."

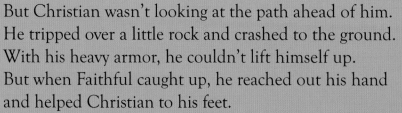

But Christian wasn't looking at the path ahead of him.
He tripped over a little rock and crashed to the ground.
With his heavy armor, he couldn't lift himself up.
But when Faithful caught up, he reached out his hand
and helped Christian to his feet.

"Finally," said Christian, "a companion for my travels!
I didn't know that you too set out for the Celestial City."

"Yes," said Faithful. "After you left, everyone was talking
about your book and the Celestial City. And after a while
they started to mock you. But I believed your book,
so I set out to follow you."

As they walked, Faithful spoke about those who tried to stop him along the way.
"There was one named Shame, who I met in the Valley of Humiliation.
Shame told me that those who listen to the King are fools
and will be looked down upon by others in this world.
But I stood against him and finally resolved that what the King says
is always best—even if everyone in the world is against it."

Christian's heart was uplifted by Faithful,
and they continued in sweet conversation.

Their conversation was interrupted by a boy named Talkative
who joined them and said, "Hello there! You're pilgrims, I see.
Let's journey together and talk along the way.
There are so many things to talk about!
Big things or little things—I can talk about them all."

Faithful interrupted him. "Our desire is not just to talk,
but to follow the King's path and reach the Celestial City."

"Ah, yes," Talkative said. "I can tell you all about that city.
I have many theories about it. We can talk about that if you wish."

Christian said, "The King wants us to follow him and obey him—
and not just talk. We must love others in deed and truth,
not just in word and speech."

"I see," said Talkative. "You pilgrims are strange.
I'll wait for others who like my company,
so I can have pleasant conversation along this path.
I'm in no hurry."

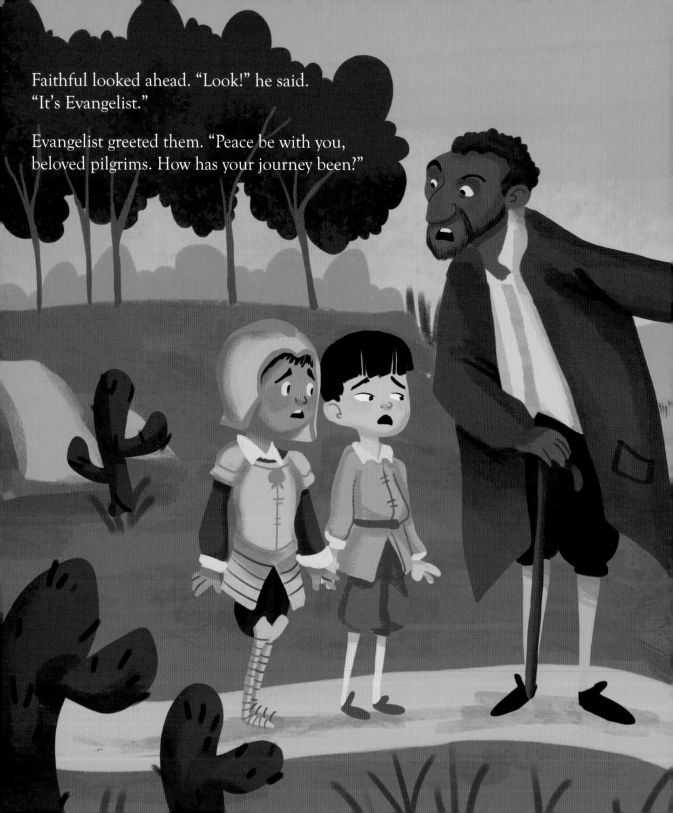

Faithful looked ahead. "Look!" he said. "It's Evangelist."

Evangelist greeted them. "Peace be with you, beloved pilgrims. How has your journey been?"

Christian answered, "The King has delivered us
from every snare that was set on our path."

"I rejoice in your victories," said Evangelist.
"But I came here to warn you. You must pass
through an evil town called Vanity Fair.
It was built by enemies of the King
to distract pilgrims on their journey."

Evangelist warned them:
"You'll be tempted there by the vanities and riches of the world.
But you must keep your eyes fixed on the Celestial City."

At first, Christian and Faithful
thought Vanity Fair looked like fun.
It looked beautiful on the outside,
but they quickly learned
it was evil on the inside.

Merchants soon surrounded them
and tried to sell them trinkets and vanities.
"Here we have everything pleasant
to eat or wear or see," they said.
"Forget your difficult journey,
and stay here where you can enjoy
all the delights of the world."

142

But Faithful stopped them and said,
"Turn my eyes away from all this vanity!"

"But you must want to buy something?" the merchants said.

"You sell only lies," said Faithful. "What you sell here will burn away like chaff. We seek everlasting treasure. We buy the truth!"

This set the whole town in an uproar.

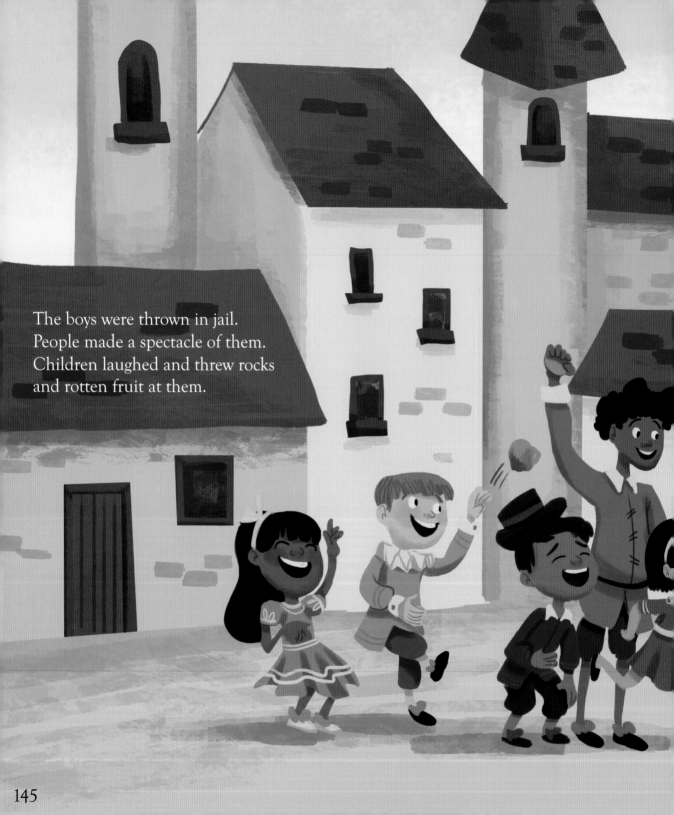

The boys were thrown in jail.
People made a spectacle of them.
Children laughed and threw rocks
and rotten fruit at them.

But Christian and Faithful
were kind to the children,
and said to them, "You don't need to stay here.
The King will welcome you to the Celestial City."

The boys were put on trial.
Their judge, Lord Hate-good, said to them,
"The witnesses here have told me
you caused a great uproar in our town,
and you don't obey the laws
of our great Prince Beelzebub.
Is this true?"

"We've caused no uproar," Faithful answered.
"We've followed only what is good and right and true.
I defy the laws of your town and your wicked Prince.
My loyalty is to the true King and his ways."

The judge slammed his gavel. "Death! Death!
I sentence them both to death!"

Back in jail, Christian and Faithful encouraged each other
with promises from the King.

Guards came and took Faithful away in chains.
Christian called out, "Faithful, don't be afraid.
They can destroy our bodies, but not our souls.
I'll see you in the Celestial City!"

A boy named Hopeful had been watching them.
When the guards weren't looking,
he took their keys.

He freed Christian from the jail.
"Let's go," he said.
"Quick, before they come back!"

As Christian left Vanity Fair, he looked up, and there was Faithful!
The King had sent a chariot to take him to the Celestial City.

"I'll miss you, faithful friend!" Christian cried out.

Hopeful comforted Christian: "Faithful's bravery inspired me to leave Vanity Fair. I hope I can be a friend like he was."

Chapter 7 Summary

In chapter 7, Christian meets Faithful, his first true companion on this journey. His new friend joined the journey because he heard about Christian leaving for the Celestial City.

Christian and Faithful must pass through Vanity Fair, which is a picture of what we read in 1 John 2:15-17, "Do not love the world or the things in the world...for all that is in the world—the desires of the flesh and the desires of the eyes and pride of life—is not from the Father but is from the world. And the world is passing away along with its desires, but whoever does the will of God abides forever."

When John speaks of the "world" he isn't speaking of the physical earth, or all the beautiful things God has made; instead, he is speaking about an unhealthy desire for possessions, pleasure, or popularity.

Though God has given us wonderful things in the world to enjoy and to thank him for, it's easy to become so focused on these things that we forget about God and heaven. Like the pilgrims, we must keep our eyes set on the Celestial City (Colossians 3:1-4). We should put our hope in the glorious future God has prepared for Christians, instead of in things that will rust and fade away (Matthew 6:19-21).

Understanding the Allegory:

1. Why is Vanity Fair so dangerous for pilgrims?
2. How do Faithful and Christian respond to the merchants?

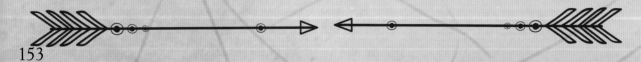

Chapter 8:

Doubting Castle

The two little pilgrims traveled a little while,
and were met by four children from the town of Love-Gain.
These four said, "Let us join you on your journey."

"Please, come along!" Hopeful said.

"But it's not an easy path," Christian told them.

"What could be so difficult about it?" one boy asked.

Christian said, "You must follow the King in sunshine and rain, in riches and poverty, in good times and hard times."

"You're sadly mistaken," said the boys from Love-Gain. "Surely the King would give all his blessings to pilgrims who walk on his path. We travel only in fair weather. If you wish to suffer needlessly, then we will not join you."

The little pilgrims left the other boys behind.
They came to a hill called Lucre.
At the top there was a silver mine,
and a man named Demas called out to them,
"Hey ho! Come behold,
riches and treasures, riches untold.
Come to my silver mine, and you shall find
a happy fortune in little time."

"Let's go see." Hopeful said.

"No way," said Christian. "This place is a trap and a snare.
It has hindered many pilgrims, because the love of money
is the root of all kinds of evil."

Demas called out again: "Come and see—it's safe and free."

"You're a liar, Demas," Christian said. "Many have died here.
When we meet the King, we'll tell him of your deceit."

When the four boys from Love-Gain came, they believed Demas.
They went to the silver mine, and as they looked into it,
they slipped and crashed to the bottom.

158

As they walked on, their path led them beside a pleasant river.
It was called the River of the Water of Life.
The two pilgrims walked here with delight.
They drank cool, clear water and ate all kinds of fruit.
They rested from their journey, and their souls were refreshed.

"The King's path is often difficult," Christian said,
"but it's full of joys that many never taste."

"Yes," said Hopeful. "These delights are far greater
than Demas's silver or the treasures of Vanity Fair."

The narrow path soon became rough and rocky.
The boys longed to return to the delightful path by the river.
Their feet were sore from their big journey,
and they became tired and discouraged.

Later they saw a smooth meadow of grass. To get to it, Christian jumped over a fence. "Let's go this way," he said.

"But what if it's the wrong way?" Hopeful said.

"It won't be," said Christian. "I can see ahead. It follows the path."

As it became dark, Christian and Hopeful were lost.
"I shouldn't have listened to you," said Hopeful.
"We should have stayed on the King's path."

"Forgive me," Christian said. "I was wrong to leave the path again,
and I should know better by now. Let's turn around and go back."

But a heavy rain flooded their path. They couldn't find their way back.
They decided to sleep there for the night, shivering in the cold rain.

They didn't know they'd fallen asleep near Doubting Castle.
They woke to the sound of a loud rough voice:
"What are you doing on my land?"

Christian was terrified.
"We're pilgrims, we're lost, and we didn't know better."

"That's no excuse for trampling on my grass!" said Giant Despair.
He picked them up and dragged them to his castle.

Giant Despair threw them into a dark and dirty dungeon.
They lay there for days without a crumb of bread
or a drop of water. They were far from family and friends
or anyone to help them.

Worse still, the Giant beat them. He yelled at them:
"You'll never get out of here! You'll die here in this prison,
so give up hope. There's no way out."

"I give up," Christian said.

But Hopeful encouraged him.
"Be patient, brother.
We must wait and hope.
Maybe someday he'll forget to lock us in."

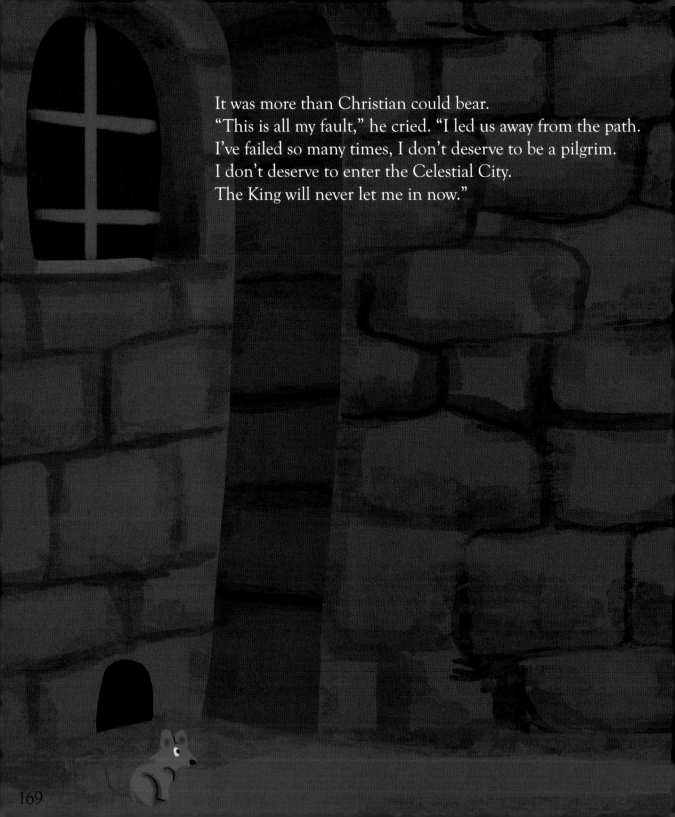

It was more than Christian could bear.
"This is all my fault," he cried. "I led us away from the path.
I've failed so many times, I don't deserve to be a pilgrim.
I don't deserve to enter the Celestial City.
The King will never let me in now."

But Hopeful said, "The King is merciful.
He'll never abandon you. We'll soon see the Celestial City.
Remember how brave you've been so far:
Apollyon couldn't crush you.
The Valley of the Shadow of Death didn't turn you away.
With the King's help, you've overcome many difficulties.
And you'll overcome this one as well."

Early the next morning, Christian woke and said,
"What a fool I've been! How could I have forgotten?
The King left a key called Promise, hidden here in my pocket!
I'm certain it will open any lock in Doubting Castle."

Christian tried the key in their door, and it worked.
Together they pushed it open.
But then, as they opened the gate leading out of the castle,
it made a loud creaking sound, which woke up Giant Despair.

The Giant chased after them. But just as he reached to grab them,
the sun pierced through the clouds and blinded him.
He fell to the ground with a huge crash.

The boys ran until they reached the King's path again.
They put a sign there to warn other pilgrims about the Castle of Despair.
They jumped back over the fence, thanking the King
for delivering them once again. They continued on the narrow path.

Chapter 8 Summary

In chapter 8, Hopeful begins the journey with Christian. They encounter four boys from the town of Love-Gain who say they want to be pilgrims. But those four will follow the King's path only when it's easy and in good weather. They represent people who follow God just to get some blessings or gain from him (2 Timothy 4:10).

Some people believe in Christianity because they think God will make them healthy, wealthy, and happy. But Jesus said, "If anyone would come after me, let him deny himself and take up his cross and follow me. For whoever would save his life will lose it, but whoever loses his life for my sake will find it. For what will it profit a man if he gains the whole world and forfeits his soul? Or what shall a man give in return for his soul?" (Matthew 16:24-26).

The boys also encounter Giant Despair, who locks them in his dungeon. This represents the discouragement Christians can experience, which at times can seem so strong it feels like we'll never be able to escape from it (2 Corinthians 1:8).

The Key of Promise represents God's promises in the Bible. Those promises have the power to free us from despair (Proverbs 4:20-22; Psalm 119:11).

Understanding the Allegory:
1. Why won't the boys from Love-Gain join the two pilgrims?
2. How do Christian and Hopeful escape from Castle Despair?

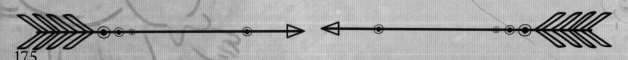

Chapter 9:

The Delectable
Mountains

The little pilgrims reached the Delectable Mountains.
They saw four shepherds looking after their sheep.

Hopeful asked them, "Whose mountains are these?"

"They belong to the King," the shepherds replied.
"This is Immanuel's Land."

Christian asked, "Are we close to the Celestial City?
Is the way safe from here?"

"It's safe for all who know and love the King," said the shepherds.
"The King leads and protects his pilgrims all the way
to the Celestial City—just as we lead and protect these sheep
beside still waters and fields of green grass."

The shepherds took Hopeful and Christian
to the top of a high hill called Clear. They asked,
"Would you like to see the gates of the Celestial City?"

"Please!" said the boys.

The shepherds gave them a telescope to look through.
What they saw of the city was so beautiful and glorious
that everything else seemed dim and dull in comparison.

As the boys left, the shepherds gave them instructions:
"Beware of the Flatterer, who'll disguise himself
and lead you astray. And beware of the Enchanted Ground,
where you'll be tempted to fall asleep.
May the King guide and protect you in all things."

The path soon split
in two directions.
Which one
should they take?

Then they saw a man in a white robe, who said,
"You look like two smart little pilgrims.
You must have come so far on your journey."

"Yes," Hopeful said, "our path has been long and difficult,
and many have turned away."

"And I had to fight with Apollyon," Christian added.

"Apollyon! You must be
very brave," said the man.
"Come with me. I'm traveling
to the Celestial City as well."

They followed the man,
but they didn't notice the net
lying along the path.

The net entangled them, and they couldn't get out.
Then the man's white robe slipped off his back,
revealing his black clothes.

"Flatterer!" the pilgrims shouted.
"The shepherds warned us about you!"

The Flatterer only laughed and walked away.

But the King sent a Shining One
who tore the net open to set the boys free.

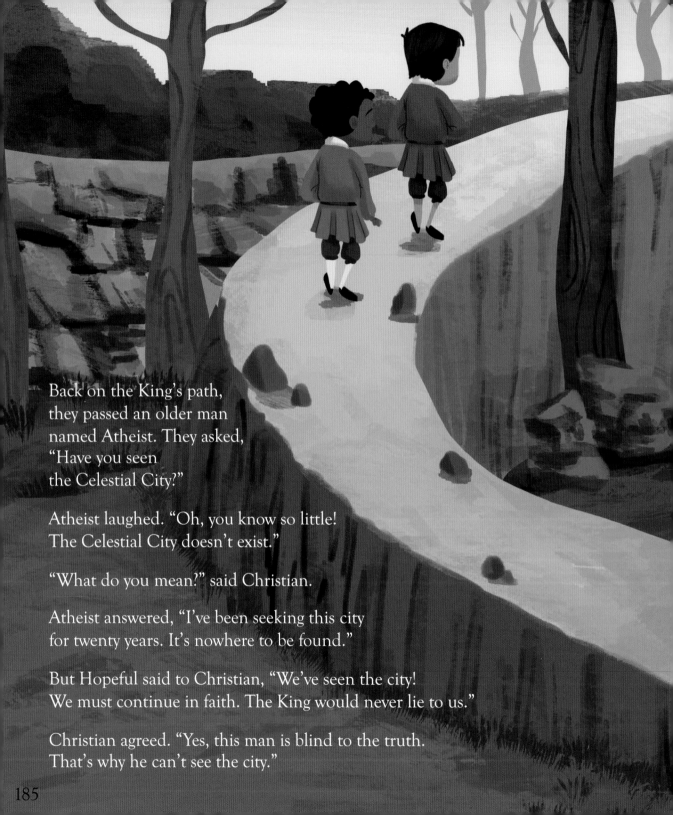

Back on the King's path,
they passed an older man
named Atheist. They asked,
"Have you seen
the Celestial City?"

Atheist laughed. "Oh, you know so little!
The Celestial City doesn't exist."

"What do you mean?" said Christian.

Atheist answered, "I've been seeking this city
for twenty years. It's nowhere to be found."

But Hopeful said to Christian, "We've seen the city!
We must continue in faith. The King would never lie to us."

Christian agreed. "Yes, this man is blind to the truth.
That's why he can't see the city."

The two boys came to a place
where the air made them drowsy. "Let's take a nap,"
Hopeful said. "I can barely keep my eyes open."

"Stay awake!" Christian said. "The shepherds warned us
about the Enchanted Ground. If we sleep here,
we may never wake up. Let's talk about our journey—
that will help to keep us awake."

"You're right." Hopeful said. "I almost forgot their warning.
It's true, two are better than one. I'm thankful to have you with me.
This path would be dangerous to travel alone."

Farther on, they saw a man walking behind them.
Hopeful asked him, "Why are you walking alone? Come join us."

The man's name was Ignorance. "I like to walk by myself,"
he said, "while I think about entering the Celestial City.
You know, my heart tells me the Celestial City is so real—
and I believe my heart."

"And why do you think the King will let you in?"
Christian asked.

"Because I have a good heart," said Ignorance,
"and I've lived a good life."

"But that's not what the King has written in his book,"
Christian said. "The only way into the city
is by believing in the King's Son and his forgiveness.
Our hearts are not good, and we're often led astray.
Only by the King's mercy can we enter the city."

"No," said Ignorance, "I'm not led astray.
I'll continue on my own. My heart
will guide me." So he left them.

Then Christian and Hopeful entered the country of Beulah.
The air here was sweet and pleasant, and they heard birds singing.
The glow of the Celestial City was like golden sunlight on the horizon.
They knew they were far beyond all the dark places on their journey,
for here the city gave light to everything all around.

Chapter 9 Summary

In chapter 9 the little pilgrims meet some shepherds, who represent church pastors who encourage and guide Christians in their journey. The shepherds are also a picture of Jesus, the Good Shepherd, who always cares for his sheep (John 10:11-18).

The shepherds give warning about the Flatterer and the Enchanted Ground. A flatterer is someone who speaks nice words but is only trying to trick us and take advantage of us: "A man who flatters his neighbor spreads a net for his feet" (Proverbs 29:5).

Hopeful nearly falls asleep at the Enchanted Ground, but Christian keeps him awake. All Christians need trustworthy friends to warn them about laziness in their spiritual life (Ecclesiastes 4:9-12).

The boys also meet Atheist and Ignorance. An atheist is someone who doesn't believe in God, and who says that there's no heaven or hell (Psalm 14:1). Ignorance represents those who think they're good on their own, and who don't believe the King's word or want to follow the King's path. Many people say they're Christians, but only those who trust in the King are truly Christians (Matthew 7:22-23). We cannot trust our hearts—they can lead us astray. We must trust God and his word (Jeremiah 17:9).

Understanding the Allegory:

1. What two warnings do the Shepherds give to the pilgrims?
2. Why is Atheist not able to see the Celestial City?

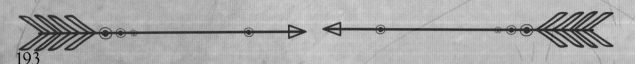

Chapter 10:

The Celestial City

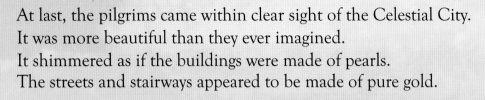

At last, the pilgrims came within clear sight of the Celestial City.
It was more beautiful than they ever imagined.
It shimmered as if the buildings were made of pearls.
The streets and stairways appeared to be made of pure gold.

This sight filled them with such longing to be there!
They ran along the path with hearts full of hope.

But their path led them to the dark river called Death.
They looked for another way across. But there was none.

"Look how deep the waters are!" Christian said.
"I don't know if we'll make it."

"But there's no other way to the city," Hopeful said.
"We must go in. The King has never failed us—
we must trust him again, as always."

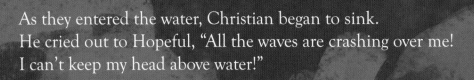

As they entered the water, Christian began to sink.
He cried out to Hopeful, "All the waves are crashing over me!
I can't keep my head above water!"

Hopeful held on to Christian. "I feel the bottom," he said,
"and it's good and solid. Let's press on!"

"I'm going to die!" said Christian. "I'll never reach the city."
He was so afraid, and he couldn't see the city's light.

Hopeful tugged Christian's head above the water.
"I see the gate," Hopeful said. "Angels are there to receive us."

Christian gasped and said to Hopeful, "They're waiting
just for you. The King has left me here to drown.
I've been such a faithless pilgrim."

Then Christian remembered the King's promise:
"When you pass through the waters, I will be with you,
and through the rivers, they will not overcome you."

Christian's strength returned. "Yes, brother, I feel the ground! You're right, it is solid. And look! The Celestial City!"

They saw two Shining Ones calling them to the city's gate.

The Shining Ones said to them,
"You're going to the Paradise of God,
where you shall eat from the Tree of Life.
You'll walk and talk with the King, forever and ever.
There'll be no more sorrow, sickness, suffering, or death,
because the former things have passed away.
The King will give you comfort for all your toil
and joy for all your sorrow. You've walked in faith,
and now you'll see all that you've desired."

The pilgrims were full of such joy! They quickly ran up the stairs.
They no longer felt tired, though their journey had been so long.

Soon they were high above the clouds. And now,
all the difficulties they'd faced in their journey seemed so small.

"I read about this in my book," Christian said.
"Now at last I see it. The King promised that one day here
is far better than a lifetime anywhere else in the world."

Christian and Hopeful entered the city's gate.
Thousands of people came out to greet them,
all singing, smiling, and dancing.
The boys heard the sweetest songs.
They felt that heaven had come down to meet them.

"We made it!" they said. "We're here!"

The Shining Ones called out,
"These pilgrims came from the City of Destruction
because of their love for the King.
Welcome in, welcome in! Eternal glory you have won!"

The little pilgrims passed their scrolls to the angels
and entered the gates with gladness.

The King also came out to welcome the two little pilgrims.
With his arms open wide, he said to them,
"Well done, my faithful pilgrims. Your journey was long,
but you've arrived at last. We've been waiting for you,
and I've prepared a place here for you.
Enter into the joy of my city!"

The pilgrims jumped into the King's arms.
At last, they knew they were home.

Chapter 10 Summary

In chapter 10, the pilgrims face one last trial when they pass through the River of Death. Christian is scared, and Hopeful encourages him. It's normal to be scared of death, but we need to remember the promises God has made to all who trust in Jesus (2 Timothy 1:10; Hebrews 2:14-15).

Christian struggles in the water, and even doubts whether he will make it to the Celestial City. But in this dark moment, Hopeful is there to encourage him (1 Thessalonians 4:16-18).

Remembering the King's promises, the two make it across and are guided up to the Celestial City. They have left behind all the sorrow and difficulties of their journey, and they step upward with joy and ease to the King's castle.

The angels there remind them of the joy awaiting them, which is the same as the joy promised to all believers in Jesus. Although our lives may be a difficult and long journey, this is nothing compared to the joy awaiting us (Revelation 21:1-5; 2 Corinthians 4:16-18).

The story ends as they're embraced in the arms of the King. Although heaven will be far better than this earth, the greatest thing will be knowing and enjoying the King (John 14:2-3).

Understanding the Allegory:

1. How does Hopeful help Christian across the River of Death?
2. What do the Shining Ones tell the boys about the Celestial City?

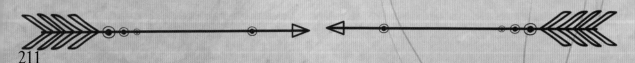

"My toilsome days are over. I am going to see
the Head that was crowned with thorns
and the Face that was spit upon, for me.
I have lived by hearsay and faith; but now I go
where I shall live by sight, and shall be with him
in whose company I delight myself; take me,
for I come to Thee."

— John Bunyan (1628-1688)

212

Epilogue

And so, we've reached the end of *Little Pilgrim's Big Journey*.

But your journey has just begun. You too can become a little pilgrim. There will be many difficulties along the way, and you'll face giants and dragons of many kinds. But the King will always be with you.

As you close this book, we pray you'll remember these three lessons:

1. *Believe the King's word*—God gave us the Bible as his perfect letter to us, to equip us and guide us on our journey. We start our journey by believing what God says about us—that we're sinners, and we need a Savior. Only Jesus can remove your burden and clothe you in his perfect righteousness (Romans 3:23, and 6:23).

2. *Follow the King's path*—Always stay on the narrow road. Many will try to lead you on the wide road, which may seem easier at times, but God has promised a great reward for all who turn from their sins and follow him (Matthew 25:34).

3. *Seek the King's city*—Christians can look forward to an eternal city far greater than we can imagine. God is preparing a place for us where we'll be happy forever. We'll be with him forever and ever, enjoying his goodness together with everyone who loves him. Never lose sight of that hope (Hebrews 11:13-16)!

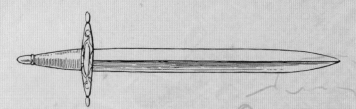

Chapter 1 Questions

Understanding the Allegory:

1. Why does Christian have a burden on his back?

2. What does Christian's book tell him?

3. How do Christian's siblings respond to his message?

4. What does Evangelist tell Christian?
   How does Christian respond?

5. Why does Obstinate try to stop Christian?
   Why won't he join on the journey?

Applying the Truth:

1. Why does sin feel like a burden? (Psalm 38:4)

2. What does it mean to believe the Bible? (Hebrews 11:1-2)

3. How would you feel if your friends or family made fun of you for believing in Jesus? (Matthew 5:11-13)

Chapter 2 Questions

Understanding the Allegory:

1. Why is Pliable excited to join Christian on the journey?

2. What happens when Pliable falls into the Bog of Despond?

3. How does Christian get out of the Bog of Despond?

4. What does Worldly tell Christian?
   Was this good advice or bad advice?

5. Why does Christian listen to Worldly?
   What happened when he followed Worldly's advice?

Applying the Truth:

1. Read Mark 4:1-20. What does Jesus teach us about
   how different people respond to the good news in the Bible?

2. How can we know who we should listen to?
   How do we tell if someone is speaking the truth? (Hebrews 4:12)

3. Why do so many people believe they can remove
   the burden of sin by doing good things?
   Where can our burdens be removed? (1 Peter 2:24)

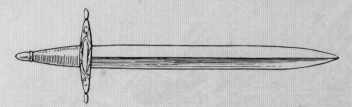

Chapter 3 Questions

Understanding the Allegory:

1. Christian was dirty and dressed in rags.
   Why did Good-Will let him in?

2. Can Christian get lost on the narrow path?

3. Why did Good-Will want Christian to meet the Interpreter?

4. What were some of the lessons that Interpreter taught to Christian?

5. Why was Passion not willing to wait for his gifts?
   What does this represent?

Applying the Truth:

1. Does Jesus accept even the worst sinners?
   Is anyone welcome to come through the Narrow Gate?
   (Matthew 11:28-30)

2. Why is the Narrow Path difficult to follow? (Luke 9:23)

3. What is the importance of having good Bible teachers? (Ephesians 4:14)

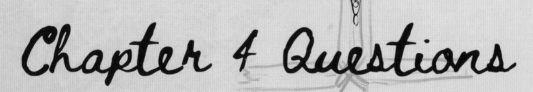

Chapter 4 Questions

Understanding the Allegory:

1. Why was Christian so eager to reach the Place of Deliverance?

2. What happened when Christian saw the cross?

3. What do the three Shining Ones give to Christian?

4. How do Slothful, Simple, and Presumption respond to Christian?

5. Why did Formalist and Hypocrisy jump over the wall of Salvation? What else did they do wrong?

Applying the Truth:

1. How can we be freed from the burden of sin?
   What should we do if we still feel guilty about our sin? (1 John 1:9)

2. Why is the cross the only place our burden can be removed?
   What do the new clothes Christian is given represent? (Isaiah 61:10)

3. What does it mean to be a hypocrite?
   Why is this a problem? (Matthew 15:7-9)

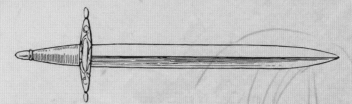

Chapter 5 Questions

Understanding the Allegory:

1. Why was Christian willing to climb up the Hill of Difficulty?

2. What was wrong with Christian sleeping so long?

3. Why did Timorous and Mistrust turn around when they saw the lions?

4. How did Christian lose his scroll?
   How did he feel when he found it again?

5. What did Discretion, Prudence, Piety, and Charity do to help Christian?

Applying the Truth:

1. Will our life become easier or more difficult when we become a Christian? (2 Timothy 3:12)

2. How can we avoid being lazy? (Proverbs 6:6-11)

3. What is the importance of being involved in a church?
   What will we lack if we don't go to church? (Hebrews 10:25)

Chapter 6 Questions

Understanding the Allegory:

1. What did Apollyon say to discourage Christian?

2. How does Christian defeat Apollyon?

3. Why does Christian enter the Valley of the Shadow of Death?

4. What did Christian hear being whispered in his ears in the Valley of the Shadow of Death?

5. How did Christian make it through the Valley of the Shadow of Death?

Applying the Truth:

1. Why does the Bible call Satan the Accuser? How can we defeat his lies? (Revelation 12:10-11)

2. What do the Helmet of Salvation, the Shield of Faith, and the Sword of the Spirit represent? (Ephesians 6:10-20)

3. What are some things you are afraid of? What can you do when you are afraid? (Psalm 56)

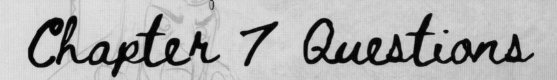

Chapter 7 Questions

Understanding the Allegory:

1. Why did Faithful leave the City of Destruction?

2. What was the problem with Talkative? Why did he stay behind?

3. Why did Evangelist warn the pilgrims about Vanity Fair?

4. Why were the merchants angry with Faithful?
   What happened to Faithful?

5. What inspired Hopeful to join Christian?

Applying the Truth:

1. What does 1 John 2:15-17 mean?

2. How can we overcome unhealthy desires for
   possessions, pleasure, or popularity? (Colossians 3:1-5)

3. Why does Jesus tell us to store up treasure in Heaven? (Matthew 6:19-21)

Chapter 8 Questions

Understanding the Allegory:

1. Why do the four boys from Love-Gain refuse to join the pilgrims?

2. How did Demas attempt to trick Christian and Hopeful?

3. Why did Christian jump over the fence to leave the Narrow Path?

4. What did Giant Despair do to the Pilgrims?

5. How did Hopeful encourage Christian?
   How do they escape from Castle Despair?

Applying the Truth:

1. If we follow God, will we always be happy, healthy, and wealthy?
   What is the problem with someone who only follows God for earthly gain?

2. What should we do when the Narrow Path becomes difficult? (Hebrews 12:1-2)

3. Christians can face seasons of discouragement and despair.
   What has God given to help us? (Psalm 42)

Chapter 9 Questions

Understanding the Allegory:

1. What two warnings do the Shepherds give to Christian and Hopeful?

2. How did the Flatterer trick the pilgrims to take the wrong path?

3. Why did Atheist tell the pilgrims that the Celestial City isn't real?

4. How did Hopeful make it through the Enchanted Ground?

5. What is wrong with Ignorance? What does he trust in?

Applying the Truth:

1. Why does God tell us to learn from and listen to godly pastors and leaders? How can this save us from error? (Hebrews 13:17)

2. How can we respond when someone says they don't believe in God, the Bible, or Heaven? (2 Corinthians 4:4; Colossians 4:6)

3. What is the importance of good friendship in the Christian life? (Ecclesiastes 4:9-12)

Chapter 10 Questions

Understanding the Allegory:

1. What does the Celestial City look like?

2. Why is Christian afraid of the River of Death? How does he make it through?

3. What do the Shining Ones tell Christian and Hopeful about the King's City?

4. How do the pilgrims feel when they enter the Celestial City?

5. What does the King say to the pilgrims?

Applying the Truth:

1. What should we do if we are afraid of death?
    How can God's promises help us to be brave? (Hebrews 2:14-15)

2. Have you read what the Bible says about the New Heavens and New Earth?
    You can read all about it in Revelation 21.

3. What will be the best part of living in the New Earth that God has prepared
    for his children? (Revelation 22:3-5)

Little Pilgrim's Big Journey
Part II is Now Available
at LithosKids.com